INDUSTRIAL HISTORY IN PICTURES: SCOTLAND

Piling and reheating wrought iron at Coats Ironworks, Coatbridge, in 1927

INDUSTRIAL HISTORY IN PICTURES:

Scotland

JOHN BUTT
IAN L. DONNACHIE
JOHN R. HUME

DAVID & CHARLES : NEWTON ABBOT

7153 4271 1

For our parents

Printed in Great Britain
by W J Holman Limited Dawlish
for David & Charles (Holdings) Limited
South Devon House Newton Abbot

CONTENTS

	page
INTRODUCTION	7
MILLS AND MILLING	9
TANNING AND LEATHERWORKING	16
BREWING	20
WHISKY DISTILLING	23
FOOD PROCESSING	30
LINEN, JUTE AND PAPER	33
COTTON AND LACE	37
WOOLLEN INDUSTRY	44
COAL MINING	51
MINING AND PROCESSING OTHER MINERALS	56
CHEMICALS	61
IRON SMELTING	67
IRONWORKING AND ENGINEERING	74
SHIPBUILDING	84
ROADS	87
CANALS	90
RAILWAYS AND TRAMWAYS	97
URBAN LIFE	101
ACKNOWLEDGMENTS	109
INDEX	111

INTRODUCTION

The intention of the authors is to present in an anthology of pictures something of the story of Scotland's industrial past. This book grew naturally from our joint efforts to record the industrial archaeology of the country. In the gazetteer of the recent *Industrial Archaeology of Scotland*, we indicated that we would illustrate in this book some of the sites mentioned there. This was the only artificial limit, apart from space, placed upon our choice of illustrations, and may help to explain the number of views of industrial buildings which appear. Yet it should be remembered that Scotland's working people spent many hours in such places. We hope that occasionally some of our selections will strike an aesthetic chord, but we did not always deliberately pick pretty pictures. Nor is the quality of some of the pictures as good as we would like; this is especially true of the older photographs which are included for their historic value. We have also tried to preserve a reasonable balance between pictures showing architectural features, machinery and people. One of our purposes, however, has been to illustrate characteristic features of industrial buildings so that readers may be encouraged to search for similar examples in their local area.

The lamentable, but natural destruction of many interesting industrial photographs, as firms modernise or die, is one explanation of the limitations of this book. We were very conscious, for instance, of the posed nature of some of the photographs which have survived. Except for recording a firm's products and leading personalities, industrial photography in earlier times was deemed to have little value. However, we hope that readers of this book will gain not only pleasure but also an appreciation of the social value of any early industrial photographs which they may possess. Local museums these days usually welcome such material.

We should perhaps say, for the benefit of historians, that the size of the sections reflects the availability of illustrations rather than our opinions on the relative importance of the industries they portray. One important omission is that of agriculture and rural crafts—except milling which is included. We excluded agriculture primarily in the hope that a full book will eventually be allocated to it.

J.B.
I.L.D.
J.R.H.

September 1967

MILLS AND MILLING

Milling has been an important rural and urban industry for centuries, and many different forms of power have been used to drive mills. Water mills were widely distributed throughout Scotland. The most primitive type, the Norse mill, is found in Orkney and Shetland, and at one time was very common in the Western Isles. More sophisticated mills, using various kinds of wheels, still survive in considerable numbers throughout Scottish counties. Many were re-equipped in the middle of last century. Though superseded for flour-milling by the large steam-driven, city roller mills from the 1850s, they are still used for milling oatmeal and animal feeding stuffs. Windmills were much rarer in Scotland than in England, there being only about one hundred in the whole country. Much more common, especially in the period 1780 to 1870 was the use of animal power, mainly for threshing, and the buildings housing these 'horsegins' are common features of the rural landscape where arable farming was once important.

A typical circular, whitewashed, stone and slate horsegin house *c* 1800 at Crossroads near Mauchline (Ayrshire)

The Norse mill at Troswick (Shetland), still in use for grinding oats for livestock in 1966. The height of the man in the photograph is 6 ft 2 in. This illustrates the typical size of these mills, which were originally built to serve family groups

Stravithie Mill, built in the eighteenth century and altered in 1856, near St Andrews (Fife) is representative of many rural grain mills in the richer and more fertile arable counties of Scotland. Note the wooden vent on the kiln

Workmen demolishing the remains of a vaulted tower windmill in Peterhead (Aberdeenshire) c 1937

A small rural mill on the river Clunie (Aberdeenshire), c 1902. Note the breast-shot wheel, the altered roof, the vane on the kiln and the miller going up to his attic granary

(Above) The most complete Scottish windmill is in Carluke (Lanarkshire) c 1797

(Left) Kingsmills (Inverness), a large burgh mill, originally water-powered, with modern pagoda-type kiln

(Above) Massive cast-iron and wood breast-shot wheel at Loudoun Mill, Newmilns (Ayrshire), still in use

(Below) Hopper and grindstones at New Cumnock Mill (Ayrshire), one of the last meal mills using water power in this county

Rebuilt on a mediaeval millstead *c* 1840, Bishop Mills, Partick (Glasgow) is a good example of nineteenth-century construction. Note the wheel house and the tailrace in the foreground and the wheatsheaf at the apex of the gable

Disused overshot wheel, 20 ft in diam, at Coldstream Mill near Beith (Ayrshire)

(Right) Sluice-gate of the Lower City Mill in Perth. This mill was later than the upper mill, being built c 1805

(Below) The upper of the two City Mills in Perth, part built before 1774 and part in the 1780s

TANNING AND LEATHER-WORKING

Many Scottish burghs had tanneries, supplying local shoe and harness makers, while from the late eighteenth century an extensive export trade in leather goods developed with America and the West Indies. Such towns as Kilmarnock, Maybole, Ayr, Lanark, Falkirk and Linlithgow and the cities of Glasgow and Edinburgh were all important leather-working centres.

Hides were first soaked in lime to remove hair and blood, then scraped and, finally, soaked for months in a mixture of tan bark, water and various noxious substances. The hides were then hung to dry, usually in draughty, wooden slatted sheds, prior to cutting and splitting. Thus, a typical tannery would have a number of stone-lined pits for steeping and characteristic stone drying sheds with wooden louvres. Concentration of leather-working developed from the mid-nineteenth century, resulting in the decay of many small units. However, leather-working survives as a handicraft in a few places like Dumfries where there are two clog-makers, but the large mechanised shoe factory is now dominant.

Lanark, a centre for the cattle trade of the Southern Uplands, had until it was recently destroyed by fire, this picturesque, if somewhat ramshackle tannery, dating in part from the seventeenth century. Note the tanner wearing protective gaiters

Ladywell Tannery, Maybole (Ayrshire), is a mid-nineteenth century structure which was closely associated with the extensive mechanised shoe-making industry in the town

An example of Glasgow's interest in leather-working, this Dalmarnock leather works is only one of several in Glasgow's industrial suburbs built after 1850

A typical small country-town tannery in Mill Street, Ayr. Still in use, it is situated conveniently close to the local slaughter house

A clogmaker's shop in Friar's Vennel, Dumfries. Note the distinctive trade sign. Most clogs made here are sold for industrial use

BREWING

A universal domestic industry, brewing was far more important than distilling in Scotland until the mid-nineteenth century. Home brewing was discouraged by the imposition of malt taxes which were inevitably and justly unpopular. In 1725 Glasgow's dissent against Walpole's malt tax burgeoned into a substantial riot. As in England, the economies achieved by large-scale production have continuously militated against small units. Edinburgh became, and has remained, the brewing capital of Scotland, while Alloa and Glasgow are also important centres. An example of the older tradition is the recently restored and now operating domestic brewhouse at Traquair House, Peeblesshire. The older breweries often incorporated maltings with characteristic pagoda-type kilns, while the narrow multi-storey brewhouses are also easily identified. The height of these buildings is severely functional, since gravity was used for the transfer of materials during the brewing process.

The large brewing complex, Croft-an-Righ (the farm of the king) Brewery, Holyrood, Edinburgh, shows on the left a malting kiln and on the right a brewhouse with ventilators and chimney

In this view of Mains Maltings, Linlithgow (West Lothian), the older portion of the structure with its single kiln is in the centre, while the more modern part on the right has twin kilns. Note the workers' housing in the left foreground which appears on a print of the 1880s

Aitken's Brewery, Falkirk, in which the malt produced at Mains Maltings was used, is a fine example of late nineteenth-century brewery architecture

The Alloa Brewery of George Younger & Son in Candlerigg Street c 1889

Port Dundas distillery (Glasgow), a large grain distillery *c* 1795 situated on the Forth & Clyde Canal, was reputedly the first Scottish distillery to use imported grain after the Repeal of the Corn Laws in 1846

WHISKY DISTILLING

Whisky is perhaps the best known Scottish product. Originally, like beer, it was produced at home for its large-scale production posed problems not solved till engineering techniques had been improved in the early nineteenth century. Proprietary brands of whisky are normally blends of malt and grain spirit. Malt whisky, however, is distilled in the traditional way in pot stills; grain spirit, which lacks any flavour, is produced by continuous distillation using a fractionating column. This differentiation of technique which developed in the 1830s has produced two sorts of distillery: the large grain distillery usually found near ports or well served at one time by canal, and the malt distillery found in areas where peat, barley and good soft water are available.

Whisky must be matured for at least three years; thus large warehouses are necessary for storage during this period. Bonded warehouses are found at distilleries and in such places as Glasgow, Dumbarton, Kilmarnock and Leith. The best container for maturing whisky is still the wooden cask, preferably one which contained sherry, so transferring a little of the colour of one drink to the other.

Islay is one of the main centres of malt whisky distillation, being famous for peat-flavoured whiskies. This print, c 1885, shows Bowmore distillery with a steamer awaiting cargo

Fife is an important malting and distilling county. Auchtertool distillery, shown here, is probably the oldest in the county

Bankier distillery (Stirlingshire) on the banks of the Forth & Clyde Canal, no longer produces whisky but, still substantially intact, serves the industry as a bonded warehouse. This print shows the horse tramway which formerly connected the distillery with the canal

Hazelburn distillery, Campbeltown, was one of many in the burgh. This illustration shows three pot stills and, on the right, a mash tun

(Left) Malting, a controlled process of artificial germination, growth and drying, develops the sugar-producing capacity of barley, so supplying a material for the malt distiller's use. Here on the malting floor at Aberfeldy distillery (Perthshire), one of the forty-one malt whisky distilleries operated by The Distillers Co Ltd, the sprouting grain is raked to preserve its condition

(Below) A mixture of malt grist and water is being fermented at Aberfeldy. This process takes thirty-six to forty-four hours

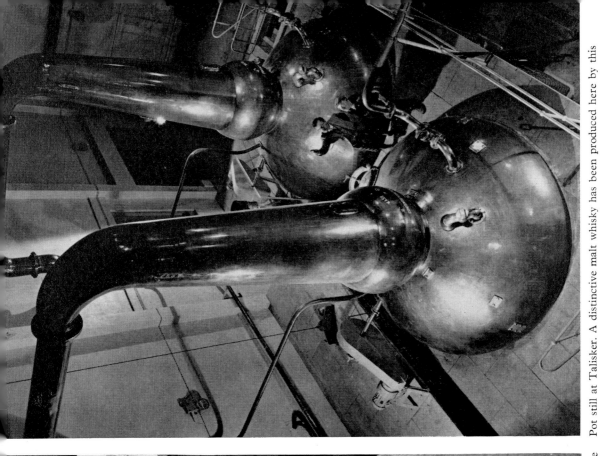

Pot still at Talisker. A distinctive malt whisky has been produced here by this process since 1830

Sampling during fermentation at Talisker distillery, the only distillery on the Isle of Skye

'Maturing in the wood', in a bonded warehouse at Carron (Morayshire). Scotch must be matured under government supervision for at least three years. DCL brands of whisky are matured for a considerably longer period

Sampling whisky maturing at Mortlach distillery, Dufftown (Banffshire). This distillery was substantially rebuilt in 1963-4

(Right) Excise office at Millburn distillery, Inverness, formerly a grain mill

(Below) Dundashill distillery (Glasgow) — a much idealised view of another large urban grain distillery *c* 1885, showing the plant layout

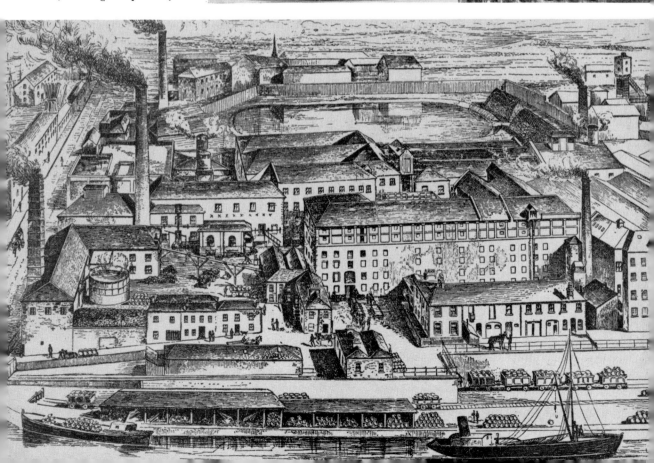

FOOD PROCESSING

The concentration of Scotland's population into towns and cities during the nineteenth century encouraged the scientific improvement of the food-processing industries—meat curing, fish smoking and salting, baking, confectionery, dairying and preserve making. Some most impressive buildings were constructed, usually in the period from 1880 to 1914, using polychrome brick to achieve startling aesthetic effects.

The United Co-operative Bakery Society (Glasgow) combined a flour mill and bakery in a large factory block whose Adelphi Street frontage is in mock Venetian style

(Top) Cranstonhill Bakery, the first steam-driven bakery in Scotland, was built by William Spence *c* 1862. It produced 'Stevenson's Machine-Made Bread', untouched by human hand

(Bottom) Buchanan's 'Sweetie Works' was one of the largest confectionery factories in Scotland, and its scale is well illustrated in this print

Salt herring was for centuries a major export from Calvinist Scotland to Catholic Europe and beyond. This illustration shows the gutting of herring at Stornoway (Isle of Lewis) c 1900

This cottage, built by a linen weaver and draper in 1723 at Kilbarchan (Renfrewshire), survived many local changes —for instance, to cotton and then to wool—and has been attractively restored by the National Trust for Scotland

LINEN, JUTE AND PAPER

Linen was the most important Scottish textile manufacture in the eighteenth century, the woollen industry having been sacrificed to the larger and more efficient English industry at the time of the Union in 1707. The remains of weavers' cottages, beetling mills and lint mills (scutching mills) are widespread. The mechanisation of the industry was slower than that of cotton, requiring as it did some special techniques. Fine weaving was concentrated in the west of Scotland, where it provided the technical basis and business organisation for the growth of the cotton industry. Coarse linen was mainly produced in the eastern counties of Fife, Angus and Kincardine. This region, but especially the towns of Dundee, Kirkcaldy and Dunfermline, became the centre of the jute industry from the 1820s.

Paper-making, well established in the eighteenth century in Midlothian and Aberdeenshire, is now also important in West Fife and Glasgow.

(Right) Beetling stocks at Alyth (Perthshire), which were used for improving the texture of linen cloth

(Below) Originally a cotton mill, Stoneyholm Mill and the adjacent Dennyholm Mill were in the 1950s the largest single linen thread producing unit in Scotland

(Right) A patient Clydesdale waits with a load of raw jute outside a warehouse in Dundee. Note the cast-iron spiral staircase

(Below) A fine example of a mid-nineteenth century, steam-driven flax-spinning mill, West Bridge mill at Linktown, Kirkcaldy (Fife)

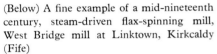

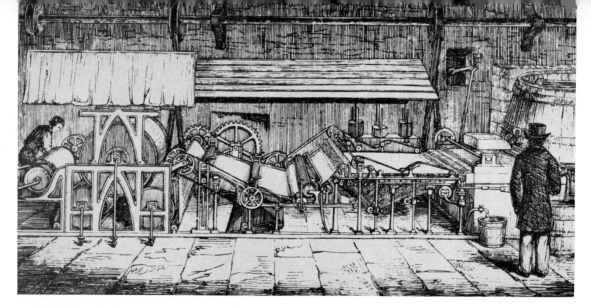

(Top) An early paper machine, indicating the relative size and cost of the capital equipment. From the vat on the right, the 'stuff' (suspended fibres) flows on to a wire gauze. It is then transferred to a felt, squeezed, and then dried on steam-heated rollers (left). The principle of the modern machine is the same, though modern machines are longer and more robustly constructed. In the right background can be seen the lever operating the sluice which controlled the flow of water to the water-wheel

(Bottom) St Leonard's Paper Works, Lasswade (Midlothian), closed in 1966. This shows a drop-valve uniflow engine, built by Hick Hargreaves of Bolton

COTTON AND LACE

From small beginnings at Penicuik and Rothesay in 1778 the Scottish cotton industry grew rapidly, and by 1838 there were 192 cotton mills in Scotland. Survivals, especially of the early water-power industry, are numerous, the best being New Lanark, Deanston, Stanley and the housing at Catrine, while at Blantyre the counting house and a tenement—now the National Memorial to David Livingstone—remain. At Rothesay, a corn mill which was probably an early cotton mill and a building now occupied by handloom weavers, possibly early workers' housing, survive. Of the later steam-driven mills, especially in Glasgow, there are more substantial remains. In Renfrewshire, early mills exist in Neilston, Barrhead, Johnstone and Bridge of Weir, but the most striking monuments are the large thread mills built at the end of the nineteenth century in Paisley and Neilston.

The lace industry of the Irvine valley was a mushroom growth from 1879, a consequence of the enterprise of Alexander Morton at Newmilns and Darvel. This very successful industry grew just when other Scottish industries were at a low ebb.

Rothesay Mill. Until recently a corn mill, this may well have been the second cotton mill in Scotland. It is now a builder's store. Note the lines of windows, some bricked in

Workers of Rothesay awake! One of the authors blows the horn (now in Rothesay Museum) which was used to call the cotton workers to the mills

The oldest surviving part of Deanston Mills (Perthshire) which was recently converted into a distillery

New Lanark Mills, made famous by Robert Owen. On the right, Owen's school and in the centre the main mill range

Interior of a worker's house at New Lanark, before conversion by the New Lanark Association. The cast-iron range is typical of Scottish dwelling houses of the period

Stanley Mills (Perthshire). Note the bell tower and the use of brick, *c* 1786. The lade system here, as at New Lanark, was tunnelled through rock for a substantial length

Counting house at Blantyre Mills, where the missionary-explorer, David Livingstone, was employed as a piecer

Mill lade and workers' housing at Catrine (Ayrshire). The houses which date from the 1780s had a second storey added during the nineteenth century. The lade now supplies a hydro-electric generating station. Unfortunately, the mills at Catrine, which were outstanding architecturally, were demolished in the early 1960s

Calderhaugh silk mill at Lochwinnoch (Renfrewshire), formerly a cotton mill

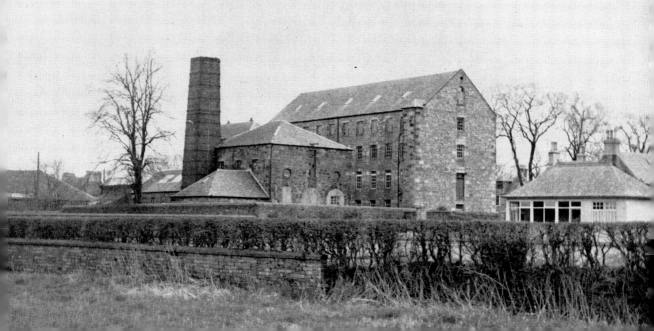

(Top) Lancefield Cotton-spinning Company (Glasgow) of W. Graham, now a bonded warehouse

(Bottom) Anchor Mills (Paisley), a classic example of mill design by W. J. Morley of Bradford

(Above) Houldsworth's Cheapside Street Mill, designed by William Creighton of Boulton & Watt in 1804 and the first attempt at fireproof building in Scotland. Note the use of pilasters to relieve an otherwise plain building

(Bottom) A typical Darvel (Ayrshire) sawtooth lace mill, originally steam driven

A woollen mill at Huntly (Aberdeenshire), still driven by water power. The mill produces high grade knitted goods

WOOLLEN INDUSTRY

The woollen industry, especially hosiery manufacture, was widely dispersed in Scotland at the beginning of the eighteenth century and although locally important, seems nationally to have declined through fierce competition from the English industry after the Treaty of Union. The rise of the fashion for tweed from the third decade of the nineteenth century and the ceremonial panoply of the Scottish regiments encouraged spectacular expansion, especially in the 1850s and 1860s when the Borders became significant. By 1878 there were 246 woollen factories of all sizes, employing 22,500 workers. From the 1840s carpet weaving became an important industry in Glasgow and Kilmarnock, while the making of bonnets and blankets were other thriving sectors of the trade.

Men at work wool-spinning at Huntly

In 1833 C. S. Cochrane introduced merino spinning to Glasgow. In the foreground is his mill, now disused. At the rear is a grain store and Bishop Garden cotton mill

Meadow Mill, *c* 1840, one of an interesting group of mills in Clackmannanshire, was closed in 1964

A group of deserted mules at Meadow Mill dating from the 1860s and 1870s

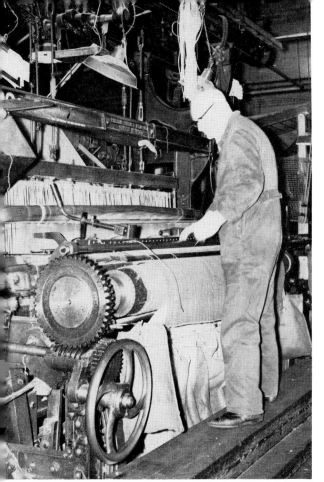

A carpet weaver at the Crownpoint Carpet factory of James Templeton & Company

Forrest Mill, Selkirk, where high quality tweeds are designed and manufactured. Note the ornate bellcote and cast-iron railings

The classical facade of Riverside tweed mills, Galashiels, owned by Braidhead & Graves

A group of factory workers in Peter Sanderson's woollen mill, Galashiels, *c* 1920

Water power at Huntly. A high-breast wheel which is the main source of power for the mill shown on pages 44 & 45

Bridgend woollen mill, Dalry (Ayrshire), a late nineteenth-century addition to an earlier mill, which has now been demolished

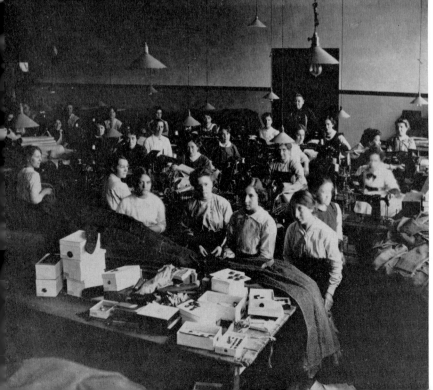

Tailoresses in J. & W. Campbell's clothing factory, Montrose Street, Glasgow, in 1914; Campbell-Bannerman, the Liberal Prime Minister, was a director of this firm

COAL MINING

From mediaeval times coal was mined in Scotland, and the difficulty of obtaining labour is illustrated by the institution of serfdom for colliers which persisted until 1799. Except in the east of Scotland mining was conducted on a small scale till the end of the eighteenth century when improvements in inland transport coupled with a great increase in demand made the exploitation of the Lanarkshire and Ayrshire seams profitable. With the growth of the iron industry in the period before 1830 output increased, but the main

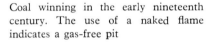

Coal winning in the early nineteenth century. The use of a naked flame indicates a gas-free pit

expansion came in the last thirty years of the century, when coal was one of the most important Scottish exports. Labour conditions in Scottish pits were poor. The employment of women and children especially in haulage was widespread but most common in the east of Scotland, and after the banning of women from underground work by statutes at first perfunctorily operated, they continued to be employed on the surface until depression affected the industry after 1920. However, the winding engine and the metal hawser had made unnecessary child and female labour underground by 1840; gradually, the pit-head gear became a characteristic feature of most collieries until recent electrification. Mechanisation of coal-winning was not extensive until after the industry was nationalised.

Harnessed 'Putters' (haulage girls) in Midlothian *c* 1842. Note the protective headgear and the leather belt for attachment to the tub

A 'Putter' in action, helped by two children *c* 1842

Before winding engines became common in Scotland, an alternative to the use of tubs was the creel or corve, carried on the back. (Left) This shows a creel-bearer *c* 1842

(Below) Detail of a winding engine at Cardowan colliery, Stepps (Lanarkshire), built by Murray & Paterson of Coatbridge in 1924

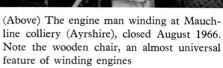

(Above) The engine man winding at Mauchline colliery (Ayrshire), closed August 1966. Note the wooden chair, an almost universal feature of winding engines

(Left) Characteristic pithead gear at Cardowan colliery, now replaced

A group of women surface workers at a Scottish colliery *c* 1900

Modern exploration of an abandoned Ayrshire 'stoop and room' mine

Miners' rows at Leadhills (Lanarkshire), built during the nineteenth century. In the left background is the village cemetery and the monument to William Symington (1764-1831), a pioneer of steam navigation who was born here

MINING AND PROCESSING
OTHER MINERALS

Scottish mining villages were usually isolated. None are more remote than Leadhills and Wanlockhead, formerly the principal centres of lead and precious metal mining in Scotland. Quarrying for lime was an important by-industry of agriculture, and many impressive farm kilns can be seen by the wayside. However, with the expansion of the Scottish iron industry, the demand for limestone as a flux was so satisfied that most accessible seams were exhausted, leaving enormous quarries behind.

An unusual extractive industry was oil-shale mining, the main centres being in West Lothian, Midlothian and Fife. Brick, tile and pottery making were once flourishing industries, although today survivals are rapidly disappearing.

(Above) Miners' rows *c* 1870 at Wanlockhead (Dumfries-shire), the highest village in Scotland

(Below) Shale-miners' rows at Addiewell (Midlothian). Compare the surroundings of previous villages with this view

(Left) The warning bell at Leadhills with a wind-vane dating from 1770. This bell was sounded to call the rescue team when disaster occurred in the mines

(Right) A water pressure beam engine at Wanlockhead, a primitive type of pumping engine, certainly used *c* 1770. Note the spoil-heap in the background

Bottle kiln, A. & W. Buchan's Portobello Pottery, dated 1906

Twin lime kilns in the gorge of the river Avon at Cot Castle near Strathaven (Lanarkshire)

Stoking the bottle kiln shown in the previous picture. Note the saggers (for protecting the pottery during the firing) in the background

Auchenheath tile works (Lanarkshire). This type of multi-vent kiln was used for the manufacture of field drains. The sheds, in the background, were used for drying the clay drains before firing

CHEMICALS

The origins of the Scottish chemical industry are hidden in the primitive household crafts of brewing, salt-boiling, soap and candle making, tanning and dyeing. The first of these to reach the status of a large-scale industry was salt-boiling which was generally connected with coal mining, the main centres being along the coastline of the Forth estuary. Demands for chemicals from the textile industries, especially for bleaching, provided the impetus for rapid growth and diversification from *c* 1750. By 1830 the Scottish chemical industry was the equal of any in the world. Vegetable oils needed by manufacturers and

Salt pans at Joppa. Prestonpans is in the left background

consumers for lubricants and lamp oil continued age-old extractive processes, although the dry distillation of coals and shales for oil, gas and tar became much more important after 1820. The large-scale processing of rubber was introduced into Scotland by American business men in 1856, despite the earlier inventive initiatives of Charles Macintosh and James Thomson, the inventor of the rubber tyre. Glass making became a speciality of Glasgow, Dumbarton, Edinburgh and Alloa in the last half of the eighteenth century, but declined with the growth of large English firms.

(Above) Alum, a principal mordant used in the textile finishing industry, was manufactured at Lennoxtown (Stirling-shire) and Hurlet (Renfrewshire). This illustration shows a boy washing the crystallised alum before it was crushed

(Below) Crushing machinery at Hurlet works *c* 1850

Sulphuric acid has been made in Scotland since 1749. (Left) This illustration shows acid pumps at Richard Smith's West Street Chemical works (Glasgow) founded in 1841

(Below) Caledonian Oil Mills, Dundee, provides vegetable oils used in batching (soaking) the raw jute

(Top) Netherplace bleachworks near Newton Mearns (Renfrewshire), founded in the eighteenth century and still in operation

(Bottom) Carpet-dyeing machine at Pullars of Perth, specially designed by their own millwrights. The building is nicknamed 'the church' on account of its previous use before the firm acquired it

Discharging coke from horizontal retorts, Maybole gasworks, July 1966

Horizontal retorts at Kirkcudbright gasworks, closed August 1967

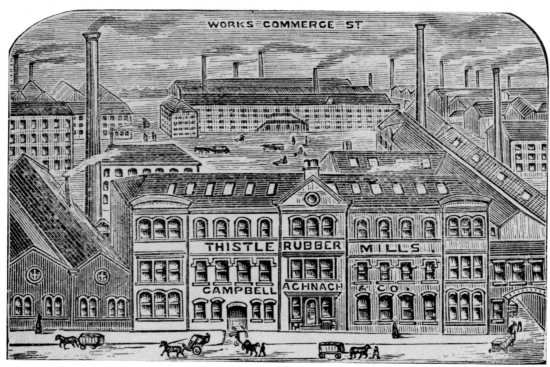

(Above) Thistle Rubber Mills, Commerce Street (Glasgow), as portrayed by a commercial artist in 1891

(Below) St Rollox Flint Glass works (Glasgow) founded 1858, now demolished

IRON SMELTING

Iron smelting has been carried on in Scotland from late mediaeval times, and the sites of many bloomeries still survive. The charcoal-smelting industry has left us with several blast furnaces dating from the eighteenth century, notably those at Bonawe and Furnace (Argyll). Coke smelting started at Carron in 1760, but the oldest surviving remains are at Wilsontown (Lanarkshire) *c* 1780 and Glenbuck (Ayrshire) *c* 1795. From the period of rapid expansion, 1830-60, surprisingly little of importance remains: the most notable features are the furnace bank and engine house at Muirkirk and the now threatened furnace bank and erecting shop at Shotts (Lanarkshire). Until very recently, a fine late-nineteenth century blast furnace plant existed at Carron (Stirlingshire).

Bonawe, oldest tenement in Argyll, associated with the charcoal-smelting company which built a furnace here in 1753

The blast furnace at Bonawe, now in the care of the Ministry of Public Buildings and Works. This is probably the outstanding industrial monument of the charcoal phase of the iron industry in Scotland

The engine houses at Wilsontown ironworks, looking across the valley of the Mouse Water from the west. The Wilsons who gave their name to this village went bankrupt in 1812, having spent over £100,000 on this works

(Above) Ore shed at Bonawe. The ore was brought from Furness by sea

(Right) The engineering shop at Carron, dating from the early nineteenth century

Sketch of Muirkirk ironworks *c* 1840

Key

1	Furnace	7	Ironstone kiln	11	Sandpit
2	Furnace	8	Coking oven	12	Manager's house
3	Furnace	9	Canal	13	Cairn Table
4	Furnace	10	Railway	14	Lower Dam
5	Forges				
6	Rolling mill				

The original blowing cylinder made by John Wilkinson in 1787, preserved there until the works was dismantled in 1930s

Rows at Muirkirk just before demolition in 1965

(Above) Furnace bank at Muirkirk with blowing engine house

(Left) Nearby are the partly buried remains of the furnace at Glenbuck *c* 1795. Smelting stopped here in 1813

(Above) Engineering shop at Shotts ironworks *c* 1825, an early instance of business integration in heavy industry

(Below) A contemporary impression of Gartsherrie ironworks in 1831, showing the first two furnaces. Here J. B. Neilson's hot-blast process was pirated. In the foreground are trains of the Garnkirk & Glasgow Railway

IRON WORKING AND ENGINEERING

A great number of foundries were established in the days before Glasgow was able to dominate Scottish ironworking as a result of transport improvements. Demand for pit tools, railway metal and locomotives, brewery and distillery equipment, machinery for many industries, structural and ornamental ironwork encouraged the development of the great Glasgow engineering firms and such enterprises in the west as Andrew Barclay, Sons & Company, Kilmarnock, now the only locomotive builders left in Scotland. Constantly, one is reminded of the astonishing versatility of the engineering labour force by the variety of products still surviving.

Barblues forge, Plains, Airdrie, one of the eight shovel forges on the North Calder water, built *c* 1840 to supply the mining companies of Lanarkshire with tools and equipment. Note the water-driven tilt hammer and the wooden crane

(Right) Rose Street foundry, Inverness. Note the typical semi-circular arched doorways, allowing easy access. Much fine iron-work for the Highland Railway was made here

(Below) Caledonia foundry, Kilmarnock, owned by Andrew Barclay, Sons & Company, a fine example of mid-nineteenth century building

Steam hammer built to Rigby's patent in 1919 at Anderson Brothers' Coatbridge engineering works, now demolished

The New Howe Machine Cycle works, Avenue Street, Bridgeton (Glasgow), built *c* 1873 to manufacture Howe sewing machines by the American firm

(Above) The Saracen foundry of Walter Macfarlane & Co, at Possilpark, the most prominent makers of sanitary and ornamental ironwork in Glasgow

(Left) The sluice-gate at Perth foundry controlling the flow of water to an undershot wheel which formerly drove the blower for the cupola

(Above) Randolph and Elder's Egyptian-style marine engineering works in Tradeston Street (Glasgow) built to the design of William Spence *c* 1860

(Below) The flywheels of the beam engine used in the rolling mill at the Excelsior Street works of John Williams (Wishaw) Ltd, now demolished

(Above) Neptune Iron, Brass & Copper works, Elliot Street, Anderson (Glasgow). Note the perpendicular style windows and the usual doorway, this time with glazed fanlight

(Below) The Argyll Motor Factory at Alexandria, Dunbartonshire, *c* 1906, an example of Edwardian business showmanship which was not backed by profit-earning capacity

(Above) Craig and Donald's machine tool works, Johnstone (Renfrewshire), whence heavy machine tools were sent all over the world

(Left) A demonstration of a rail-bending machine built for the San Paulo Railway by Craig and Donald in 1926

The Albion Motor Company's assembly shop in Finnieston Street (Glasgow) in 1901

A 1901 Albion 8 hp chassis with a two-cylinder horizontally opposed water-cooled engine and tiller steering

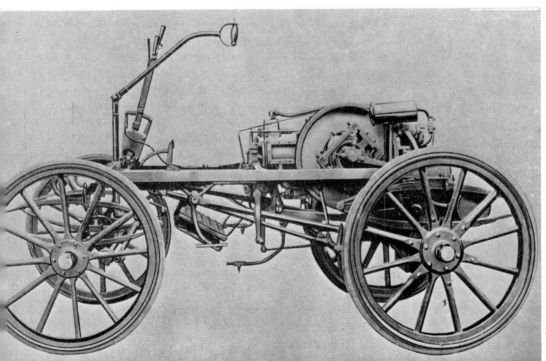

(Above) The showroom at Saracen foundry *c* 1890, indicating the wide range of products

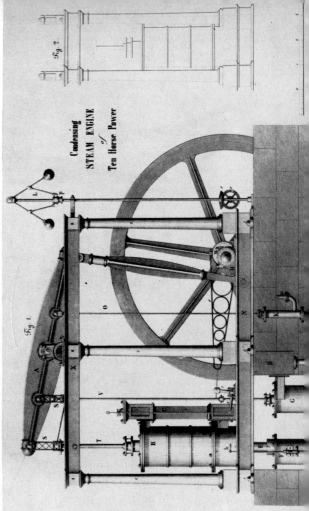

(Right) Engraving of a beam engine, typical of many built and used in Glasgow. This example was built by Mitchell & Neilson in the 1840s

Mallet compound locomotive built at the Hydepark works of the North British Locomotive Company for the South African Railways in 1914, with the men who built it. Apart from Beardmore's, also a Glasgow firm, NBL were the only British company to build Mallet locomotives

SHIPBUILDING

The development of the Clyde shipyards was most rapid after 1870, mainly as a result of expanding world commerce. Whereas in 1862 Scottish shipyards as a whole produced only 69,967 tons, by 1913 they led the world producing 756,800 tons. Yet many Glasgow firms such as Fairfields had very old origins. Their most rapid period of growth coincided with two revolutions—from wood to iron and steel and from sail to steam—which established a temporarily large market for ships, bolstered after 1900 by Admiralty orders.

The first marine engine built by Robert Napier for the *Leven*, a paddle-steamer which plied between Dumbarton and Glasgow in the 1820s

Riveting deck plates on the *Tuscania* (ship no 595) built for the Anchor Lines' Mediterranean and New York service by the Fairfield Shipbuilding & Engineering Company (launched 4 October 1921; sailed 7 September 1922)

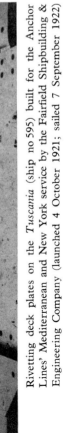

The *Montrose*, also a Fairfield vessel (ship no 529) on the stocks at their Govan yard in 1920. This ship was built for the Canadian Pacific Ocean Service Limited and used on its Pacific service

(Above) Party assembled at Fairfield's yard for the launch of the *Ermine* (ship no 486), 15 July 1912. Built for G. & J. Burns Ltd, for their Ardrossan-Belfast service, but torpedoed and sunk in the Mediterranean in 1917

(Left) The deserted cranes at Simons and Lobtnitz' Renfrew yard. This firm specialised in dredger building

ROADS

Long before the eighteenth century travellers commented on the shocking state of highways in Scotland. Few mediaeval trackways can be traced, although associated pack bridges like those at Ceres (Fife) and Biggar (Lanarkshire) provide simple monuments of the period. The greatest era of activity in road building began in the latter half of the eighteenth century with the creation of networks of military highways in the Highlands and the establishment of turnpike trusts throughout the Lowlands. Roadside survivals include bridges, tollhouses and milestones—Ayrshire, Lanarkshire, Fife and Inverness-shire provide many outstanding examples. The greatest civil engineer of the time, Thomas Telford, was responsible for much bridge and road construction, as well as numerous harbour works.

Bishop Bridge over the Ceres burn, 22 ft in span but only 6 ft wide, is probably a seventeenth-century structure at an older bridging point

General George Wade's five-arched bridge (300 ft long) at Aberfeldy (Perthshire) carries the Aberfeldy to Rannoch road (B846) over the river Tay

Baidlin tollhouse near Auchtertool (Fife). The pantiles are typical of this county, which is rich in turnpike relics

(Above) Telford's Craigellachie bridge (160 ft span) over the Spey, built in 1815, was a fine example of early cast-iron construction. The span has been carefully replaced in steel to preserve its pristine appearance

(Below) Two of the arches of Telford's Dean Bridge, Edinburgh (completed in 1831), the finest urban viaduct in Scotland. This bridge was nicknamed the 'Bridge of Sighs' because of the number of suicides, and eventually the parapet had to be heightened

CANALS AND HARBOURS

Scotland did not invite the attention of the canal promoters until the end of the eighteenth century, although earlier schemes made light of the natural difficulties likely to be encountered in most of the country. However, from mediaeval times, artificial harbours were created to supplement the numerous natural havens. The estuaries of the rivers Forth, Clyde and Tay and the Cromarty, Moray and Solway firths all attracted the attention of the harbour builders—St Andrews, Crail, Ballantrae, Kirkcudbright and Banff are typical of many small harbour works. Larger ports were constructed from the end of the eighteenth century, being associated with such men as Telford, Smeaton and the Rennies. Canals tended to follow natural lines of communication: the Forth-Clyde valley, the Great Glen and the Crinan isthmus. Yet a few were built on the English pattern, such as the Aberdeenshire, the Glasgow & Ardrossan, and the Monkland. Only the Caledonian and Crinan canals survive as useful, though unprofitable, links.

Wyndford lock, the eastern end of the summit level on the Forth & Clyde Canal. Note Bankier distillery in the background and lock and bridge-keeper's cottage in the foreground

(Above) Forth & Clyde Canal bascule bridge and workers' cottages at Cadder (Lanarkshire)

(Below) The canal again, at Maryhill (Glasgow), looking from the locks at the western end of the summit level to the four-arched Kelvin aqueduct

(Above) Near Port Elphinstone, Inverurie —a stretch of the abandoned Aberdeenshire canal, which was built between 1797 and 1807 to the designs of John Rennie

(Right) A crane at Muirtown wharf, on the Caledonian Canal at Inverness. The ship in the background, the *Scot II*, plies for pleasure sailings on the canal

(Above) *Lochalsh II*, a maintenance boat, on the Caledonian Canal at Muirtown

(Below) The remains of Lock 2 on the Forth & Clyde Canal at Grangemouth, its eastern terminus

(Above) The canal basin at Bowling, the western terminus of the Forth & Clyde Canal. Note the customs house near the swing bridge carrying the Lanarkshire & Dumbartonshire Railway over the canal. The opening of the canal took place here in 1790, with the ceremony of emptying a hogshead of Forth water into the Clyde

(Below) The old pier at St Andrews (Fife), typical of many fine old harbours in the East Neuk. Note the drystone masonry. Until the early years of this century, St Andrews was an important fishing port. Now only pleasure boats and lobster fishers disturb its waters

(Above) The port of Glasgow in the 1880s

(Right) The East and West Piers, Leith, c 1883

page 95

A still day at Portpatrick. The first pier was erected here in the period 1774-78, improved by John Smeaton in the 1790s and later by John Rennie and his son from 1821. After 1874 Stranraer displaced Portpatrick

RAILWAYS AND TRAMWAYS

In the eighteenth century the wagonways serving the Scottish collieries presaged the great developments of the nineteenth century. By the 1830s, with the opening of the Garnkirk & Glasgow Railway and the Dundee & Newtyle, east and west Scotland were on the eve of unification through a new form of transport. The great jealous age of the Glasgow & South Western and the Caledonian, with their conflict for mineral traffic and later for passengers and steamer services, was the apogee of the railway in Scotland. Opulent

The Avon viaduct on the Edinburgh & Glasgow Railway, near Linlithgow, opened in 1842

railway hotels, ostentatious booking concourses, and even the settlement of railway staff at places like Carstairs Junction, Riccarton, Inverurie and Corkerhill reflect this great railway influence on Scottish society. At the end of the nineteenth century, the expansion of cities and the growth of a commuting population encouraged the development of new systems of transport. The tramcar began to produce a folk lore of its own!

(Above) Newtyle station on the Dundee & Newtyle Railway, dating from the 1830s. This station was closed to all traffic in 1965 and is now used as a barn by a local farmer

(Below) Union Street viaduct in Aberdeen, showing coaches of the Great North of Scotland Railway and an early electric tram

Workers' housing at Corkerhill, built by the Glasgow & South Western Railway for the enginemen, *c* 1900

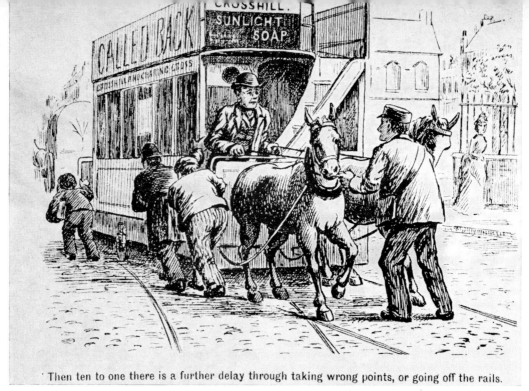

'Then ten to one there is a further delay through taking wrong points, or going off the rails.

(Above) A humorous artist's comment on the Glasgow horse trams in the 1890s

(Below) Princes Street, Edinburgh, c 1906, showing cable trams, the North British Station Hotel and in the right foreground, the roof garden above the Waverley market

URBAN LIFE

Population growth and technical change altered the mode of life of the vast majority of Scotland's people. Market towns and estate villages like Beauly (Inverness-shire) and Inveraray (Argyll), it is true, jogged quietly along in an essentially agrarian environment. Moreover, the fisher-crofting villages of the Highlands and Islands enjoyed a hard-won but very temporary prosperity during the late nineteenth century. In municipalities like Edinburgh, Glasgow, Aberdeen and Dundee old ways occasionally survived (like the fish-wives of Newhaven who sold their wares in Edinburgh); yet a new urban society had been created from the maelstrom of earlier class struggles and prejudices. 'Gas and water socialism' gradually undermined the complacency which allowed the juxta-position of industry and housing. Victorian wealth, earned by all sections of the community—if not enjoyed by all—occasionally found social outlets in the building of new civic amenities. After 1900 the motor car increasingly introduced danger and sometimes confusion into an urban society more used to human and animal than scientific power. Despite the obvious stark contrasts between town and country, the impression of urban life c 1900 which appears to be most accurate is one of congestion and piece-meal changes; the motor car jostled the horse and cart and the bicycle, and all three were jostled by buses and trams.

High Street, Dundee, c 1906, showing on the right the old Town House, built by the elder Adam, demolished in the 1930s, and in the centre St Paul's Episcopal Cathedral by G. G. Scott. Note the tramcars

(Above) Inveraray (Argyll), a fine example of a planned estate village, laid out in the eighteenth century by the Duke of Argyll

(Left) In contrast, a Glasgow street scene looking up Buchanan Street from St Enoch's Square, *c* 1914

page 102

(Above) Traffic on Jamaica Bridge, Glasgow, c 1914, indicating that urban congestion is not entirely a new phenomenon. Note St Enoch's Station Hotel (right background)

(Left) Cowgate, Dundee, c 1908. Note in the right background Lower Dens Jute Mills of Baxter Brothers

(Above) Old houses and nineteenth-century tenements in Blackscroft, Dundee. The existence of these old houses was a thorn in the flesh of the sanitary authorities, and they were demolished from the 1890s

(Below) Water Row, Govan, a group of eighteenth-century cottages with the 'soor milk cairt' at the door. Note the shipbuilding yards in the background

(Above) The Square, Beauly, indicating the more leisurely pace of life in the Edwardian north

(Below) South Beach looking east, Stornoway, capital of Lewis, a prosperous Victorian town

Early arrivals at the harbour! Newhaven fish-wives in conversation

(Right) Italian immigrant poses for the family album c 1914

Newcomers to Scotland: (Left) Irish pedlars in Lanark in the 1920s.

(Above) 'Doon the watter' went Glasgow working men for recreation and Glasgow businessmen for homes. Paddle steamers at Greenock Princes Pier, the *Minerva*, a G & SW steamer, in the right foreground. Note the Italianate architecture, a feature of the design of the period

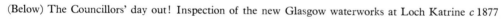

(Below) The Councillors' day out! Inspection of the new Glasgow waterworks at Loch Katrine *c* 1877

ACKNOWLEDGMENTS

We could not have compiled this book without the generous assistance of a large number of individuals, firms, and organisations. To all of these, who provided illustrations, we are deeply grateful:

Albion Motors Ltd (for 81A and B)
G. H. Brebner and the Peterhead Public Library (for 11A)
A. & W. Buchan of Portobello Pottery (for 60A)
Joseph Buckman (for 55A)
Campbells & Stewart & McDonald Ltd (for 50B)
Richard Dell, Glasgow City Archivist (for 102B and 103A)
The Distillers Co Ltd (for 26A and B, 27A and B, 28A and B)

Dundee Public Libraries and Bruce Lenman (for 103B and 104A)
Fairfields (Glasgow) Ltd (for 85A and B, 86A)
Brett Fraser (for 44, 45A and 49)
David McCardel (for 70 and 71A)
Trevor Rees (for 15B, 39A, 72A and B)
Scottish Machine Tool Corporation and J. Bennie (for 80B)
Strachan Thomson (for 55B)
James H. Treble (for 48B)
T. W. Ward Ltd (for 86B)
Stanley Wood (for 10A)

Photographs 69B, 88A and 89A are Crown Copyright and are reproduced by permission of The Controller, HM Stationery Office. They were taken for the National Monuments Record of Scotland, and we are grateful to Miss Catherine Cruft for her constant and prompt cooperation.

In addition, we would like to thank the following for helping in various ways: Carron Company; R. B. Haddon; James Houston; C. Hope Hume; Dorothy Marshall; The National Coal Board, and especially the managers of Cardowan and Mauchline Collieries and of Shotts workshops; James Porteous & Co; Pullars of Perth; James Reid; John Robertson; The Scottish Gas Board, especially the managers of Kirkcudbright and Maybole Gas Works; Norma Stewart; John Strawhorn; John Swarbrick; James Templeton & Co; John Williams (Wishaw) Ltd; William Wolfe.

Illustrations were also taken from the following books:
A. Barnard, *The Whisky Distilleries of the United Kingdom*, 1887 (24A, 25A and B, 29B), and his *Breweries of the United Kingdom*, 1889-91 (22A)
G. Buchanan, *Account of the Glasgow & Garnkirk Railway*, 1832 (73B)
John Leng & Co, *Bonnie Scotland*, 1906 (2, 11B, 32, 98B, 100B, 101, 105A and B, 108A)
S. Muspratt, *Chemistry . . . as applied and relating to the Arts and Manufactures*, 1860 (62A & B)
Royal Commission on Children's Employment, 1842, XVI (51, 52A and B, 53A)
David Scott, *The Engineer and Machinist's Assistant*, 1850 (82A)
Stratten's Glasgow and its Environs, 1891 (31B, 66A, 77B, 82B)
Thomas Annan and James M. Gale, *Glasgow Corporation Water Works*, 1877 (108B)

Our illustrations were chosen from a much larger collection. Many firms and a few individuals are not mentioned in our preceding remarks, because we had reluctantly to discard many excellent items, but we are, nonetheless, grateful to all who helped in the preparation of this anthology.

We are also grateful for the support of Professor S. G. E. Lythe and for the help provided by C. G. Wood and the Staff of the Andersonian Library, particularly for the great assistance provided by David Kennedy who made many of the prints and copies used in this book. We would also like to thank the Staffs of the University of Glasgow Library and of the Mitchell Library.

Enid Butt not only encouraged the enterprise but also typed a substantial portion of the final draft, and we are most grateful to her.

RELEVANT BOOKS

J. Butt, *The Industrial Archaeology of Scotland,* 1967

R. H. Campbell, *Scotland since 1707,* 1965

W. H. Chaloner and A. E. Musson, *Industry and Technology,* 1963

H. Hamilton, *The Industrial Revolution in Scotland,* 1966

J. Thomas, *Scottish Railway History in Pictures,* 1967

INDEX

Aberdeenshire, 11, 33, 44-5, 49, 92, 98
Argyll, 25, 67-9, 102
Ayrshire, 9, 13, 16-18, 41, 43, 50, 54-5, 65, 70-2, 75

Bakeries, 30-1
Banffshire, 28, 89
Brewing, 20-2
Bridges, 87-9
Bute, 37-8

Canals:
    Forth & Clyde, 23, 25, 90-1, 93-4
    Caledonian, 92-3
    Aberdeenshire, 92
Car industry, 79, 81
Carpet factory, 47
Chemicals, 61-6
Clackmannanshire, 22, 46
Clog making, 19
Clothing factory, 50
Coal mining, 51-5
Confectionery, 31
Cotton mills, 37-43

Distilling, 23-9
Dumfries, 16, 19, 57-8
Dunbartonshire, 79, 84
Dundee, 35, 63, 98, 101, 104

Edinburgh, 20, 59-60, 61, 89, 95, 100
Engineering:
    Foundries, 74-6, 77, 82
    Machine tools, 80
    Marine, 78, 84
    Railway, 83

Fife, 10, 24, 33, 35, 87-8, 94
Fishing, 32, 106

Gas works, 65
Glasgow, 14, 17, 23, 29-31, 42-3, 45, 47, 50, 63, 66,
    76-9, 81-3, 85, 95, 100
Glass works, 66

Harbours, 94-6
Horizontal mill, 10
Horse-gin, 9
Housing, 21, 33, 39, 41, 56-7, 67, 71, 99, 102

Inverness, 12, 29, 75, 92-3
Ironworks:
    Bonawe, 67-8
    Furnace, 67

Gartsherrie, 73
Glenbuck, 72
Muirkirk, 70-2
Shotts, 73
Wilsontown, 68
Islay, 24

Jute, 35

Kirkcudbright, 65

Lace, 43
Lanarkshire, 12, 16, 39-40, 53-4, 56, 58-60, 68,
    73-4, 76, 78, 91
Lead mining, 56-8
Lime kilns, 59
Linen, 33-5

Midlothian, 33, 36, 52, 57
Morayshire, 28

Paper making, 33, 36
Peebles, 20
Perthshire, 15, 26, 34, 38, 40, 64, 77, 88
Portpatrick, 96
Pottery kilns, 59-60

Railways, 97-9
Renfrewshire, 33-4, 41-2, 62, 64, 80, 86
Roads, 87-9
Rubber manufacture, 66

Salt pans, 61
Selkirkshire, 47-8
Shale mining, 56-7
Shetland, 9-10
Ship building, 84-6
Silk mill, 41
Skye, 27
Stirlingshire, 22, 25, 62
Stornoway, 32, 105

Tanning, 16-18
Tile works, 60
Toll-house, 88
Tramways, 100

Water mills, 9-15, 49
Water works, 108
West Lothian, 21, 97
Windmills, 11-12
Wool, 44-50